The Very Best of
Fred

The Very Best of Fred is the definitive
collection of the best cartoons featuring
Fred and his world of suburban
surrealism. Here we trace his antics
through the wittiest cartoons taken
from all four books that have featured
Fred, Penelope and their weird and
wonderful friends and relations. The
popularity of Fred continues to grow,
reflecting the enthusiasm and talent
that Rupert Fawcett has always
brought to the humour and artwork of
every cartoon.

Statics (London) Ltd
41 Standard Road, London NW10 6HF

First published by Statics 1994

Printed in England by HPH Print Ltd.
Royal London Estate, 29 North Acton Road.
London NW10 6PE

ISBN 1-873922-23-X

The Very Best of

Fred

RUPERT FAWCETT

STATICS BOOKS

FRED HAD ALWAYS SUSPECTED THERE
WAS ANOTHER SIDE TO MRS NESBIT

EVERYBODY POINTED TO THEIR
FAVOURITE PART OF THE WALL.

PENELOPE WONDERED HOW LONG
IT WOULD TAKE FRED TO NOTICE
HER NEW HAIRSTYLE

FRED WISHED BOB WOULD JUST LEAVE
IT ON THE STEP LIKE OTHER MILKMEN

FRED ALWAYS INSISTED ON
HELPING WITH THE GROCERIES

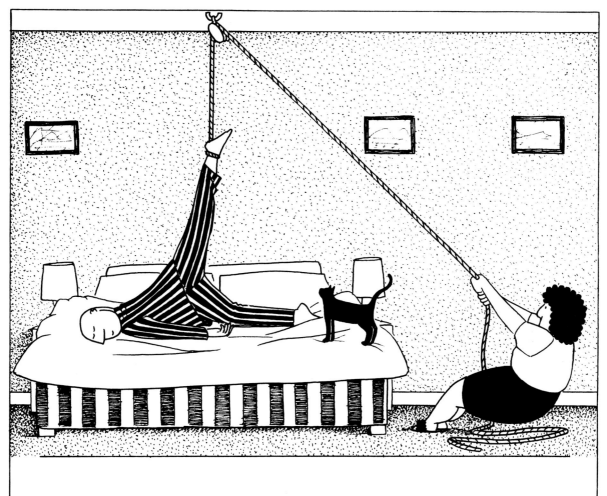

FRED HAD NEVER BEEN
A MORNINGS PERSON

FRED GREW ACCUSTOMED TO
PENELOPE'S TANTRUMS

FRED FOUND WINNING AT CHESS
IMMENSELY GRATIFYING.

PIP WAS BEGINNING TO WISH
HE'D NEVER MENTIONED
THE MOTH

FRED SPENT THE EVENING ADMIRING
HIS CORNFLAKE COLLECTION.

FRED SENSED THAT ALL WAS
NOT WELL WITH PIP.

FRED WAS ALWAYS REWARDED
FOR HELPING WITH THE GROCERIES

FRED COULD FEEL A
NOVEL COMING ON.

FRED WAS FAMOUS FOR HIS
CHRISTMAS BARBECUES

FRED SPENT MANY HOURS RESEARCHING HIS FORTHCOMING BOOK, 'A DAY IN THE LIFE OF A TABLE'

FRED OFTEN WONDERED WHY A GOOD-
LOOKING CHAP LIKE PENELOPE'S COUSIN
FRANK NEVER HAD ANY GIRLFRIENDS

FRED'S POND WAS AN ENDLESS
SOURCE OF PLEASURE TO HIM.

FRED HAD BEEN WARNED ABOUT
LEAVING THE LAVATORY SEAT UP

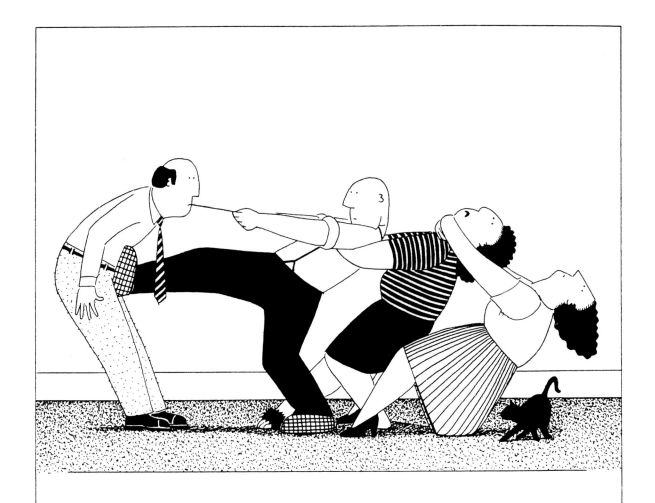

THE DENTAL FLOSS WAS
WELL AND TRULY STUCK

'ONE WINE GUM AND HE'S ANYBODY',
GROANED PENELOPE

FRED'S PRESENT CAME FROM HIS
FAVOURITE GENTLEMAN'S BOUTIQUE

FRED TRIED NOT TO
STARE AT OSCAR'S HEAD.

FRED SPENT THE EVENING WORKING
OUT HOW MUCH MONEY HE HAD SAVED
BY DOING THE PLUMBING HIMSELF

'DON'T BOTHER PUTTING YOUR
PYJAMAS ON', SIZZLED PENELOPE

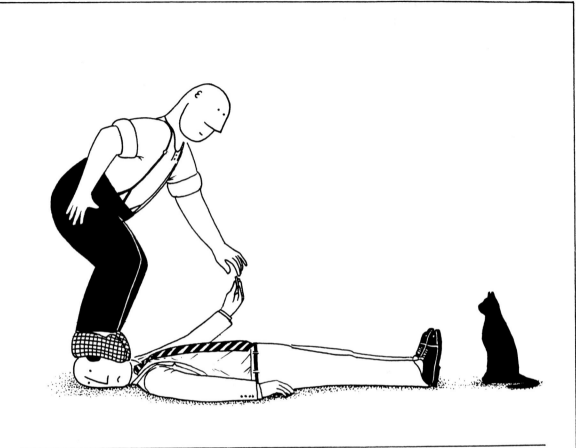

PIP GENEROUSLY AGREED TO
LEND FRED FIFTY PENCE

'LAST WEEK IT WAS MARLON BRANDO, THIS WEEK MICHAEL CAINE', WHISPERED PENELOPE

PENELOPE WONDERED IF BUNTY
MIGHT BENEFIT FROM A MORE
SUBTLE APPROACH

FRED FINALLY CONFESSED TO
EATING THE SOFA.

FRED OFTEN WISHED PENELOPE
HADŃT INTRODUCED PIP TO HER
ASSERTIVENESS TRAINING CLASSES

'I BLAME ELTON JOHN',
WHISPERED PENELOPE

'HANDS UP WHO LOVES ME',
COMMANDED PENELOPE

'SO THIS IS THE SIXTY-NINE
POSITION', SAID FRED GRIMLY.

FRED SAT DOWN TO ENJOY
A SPOT OF LUNCH.

FRED DIDN'T LIKE BIG
DISPLAYS OF EMOTION

FRED'S WAVE MACHINE TOOK THE
EFFORT OUT OF FAREWELLS

AFTER LUNCH EVERYONE SAT DOWN TO
READ THEIR CHRISTMAS PRESENTS

FRED WAS EXPERIENCING THE FAMOUS
'BOBBLE-HAT EFFECT'

PIP WAS BECOMING SUSPICIOUS
ABOUT FRED'S SO-CALLED
LUCKY STREAK

FRED ASKED CONSTANCE
AND PIP NOT TO WALK
ON THE NEW CARPET.

NOBODY EVER SAID A WORD ABOUT
MRS NESBITS LITTLE PROBLEM

FRED LOVED TO CURL UP
WITH A GOOD BOOK

FRED WAS DETERMINED TO PUT THE
YEARS OF UNEMPLOYMENT BEHIND HIM

PIP LOOKED ALL SET TO WIN THE
DOG-OWNER LOOK-A-LIKE CONTEST

FRED AND PENELOPE PROVIDED
THEIR GUESTS WITH AFTER-
DINNER ENTERTAINMENT.

'HE'S ALWAYS LIKE THIS FOR A FEW HOURS AFTER HIS OBEDIENCE CLASS, THEN IT'S BACK TO HIS OLD WAYS', SIGHED MR NESBIT

'NO BANANA HAT — NO DINNER', RULED FRED.

PENELOPE HAD FOUND
HER VOCATION

AS USUAL THE MEN SPENT THE
EVENING TALKING BALLS

'SHE'S HAVING ONE OF HER FAT AND UGLY DAYS', REPORTED FRED

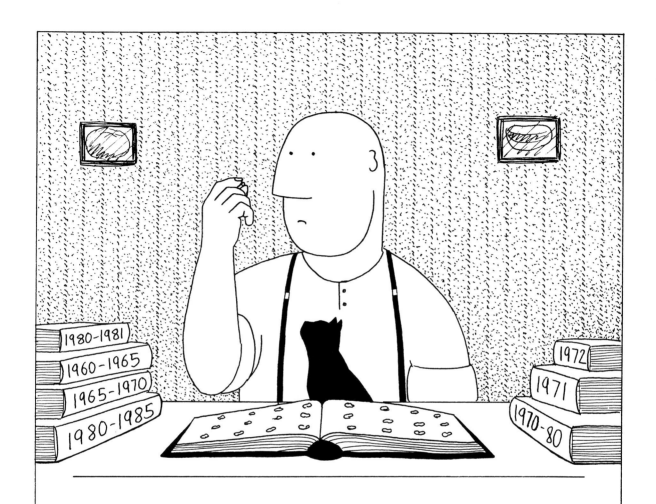

FRED WAS HORRIFIED TO DISCOVER A RICE CRISPY
IN HIS CORNFLAKE COLLECTION

FRED ASKED MR AND MRS NESBIT
TO LEAVE VIA THE SECRET TUNNEL.

BUNTY ALWAYS SPENT HOURS
DRESSING FOR A PARTY

FRED'S QUICK REFLEXES SAVED
THE SAUSAGE ROLLS.

FRED WAS DELIGHTED WITH HIS NEW
SWAMP-EFFECT CARPET

AT TIMES THE TABLE FOOTBALL
COULD GET QUITE DIRTY

FRED WAS READY FOR
THE CAROL SINGERS

FRED 'FLOSSED' HIS GUESTS
BETWEEN EACH COURSE.

PENELOPE HATED TO BE DISTURBED
DURING HER FAVOURITE SOAP

AFTER DINNER FRED
SHOWED EVERYONE THE
UNEXPLODED BOMB.

FRED LIKED NOTHING MORE THAN A
RELAXING AFTERNOON'S FISHING

PENELOPE WONDERED WHAT SORT
OF RESTAURANT FRED HAD IN MIND FOR
THEIR ROMANTIC VALENTINE DINNER

'NOT ANOTHER FULL MOON,'
GROANED PENELOPE.

IT WAS WAY PAST FRED'S BEDTIME